D1416740

LEGO® LEGENDS OF CHIMA™

OFFICIAL GUIDE

by Tracey West

SCHOLASTIC INC.

ISBN 978-0-545-54086-5

12 11 10 9 8 7 6 5 4 3 2 1 13 14 15 16 17 18/0

Printed in China 95
First printing, September 2013

MIX
Paper from responsible sources
FSC www.fsc.org FSC™ C009967

CONTENTS

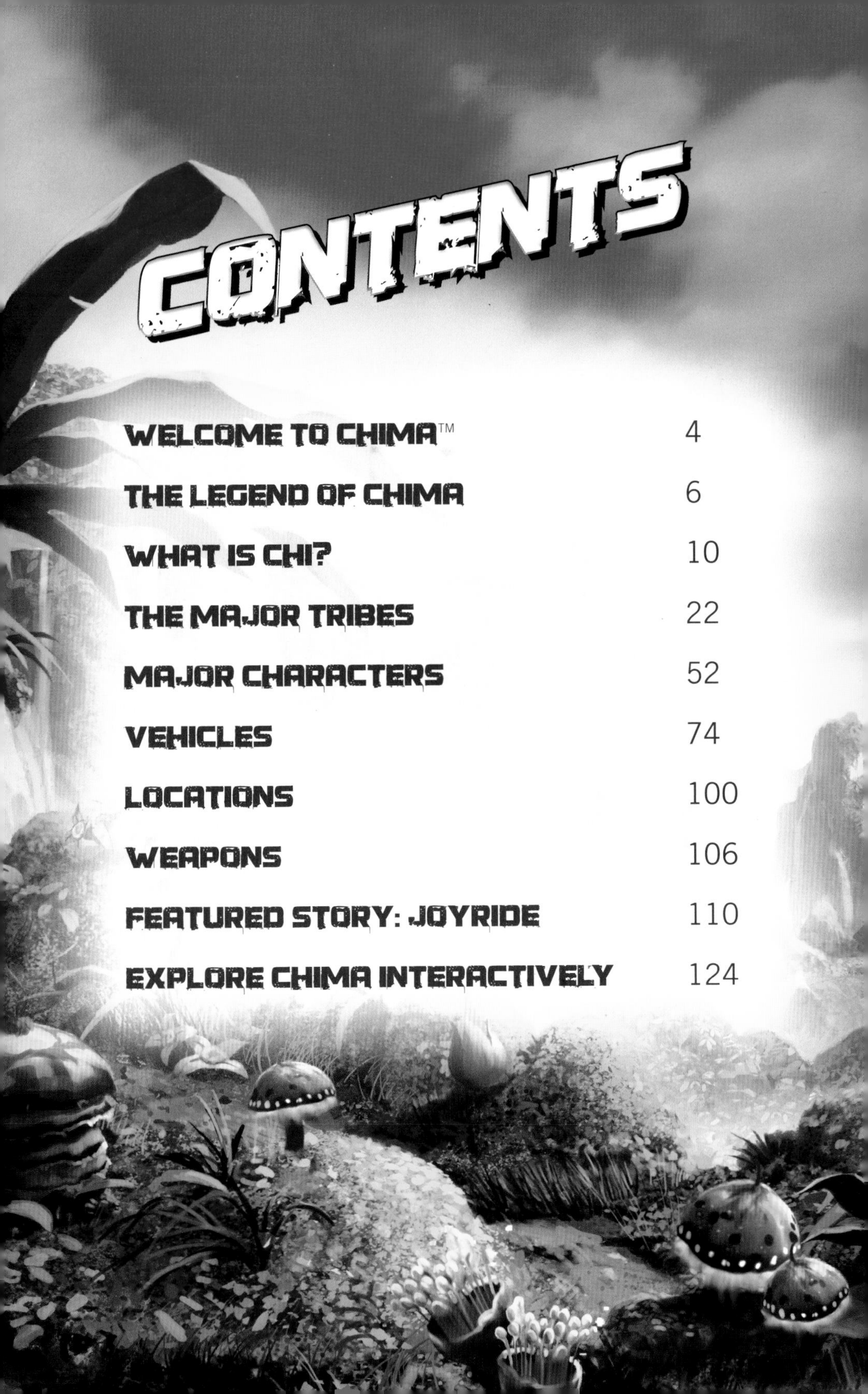

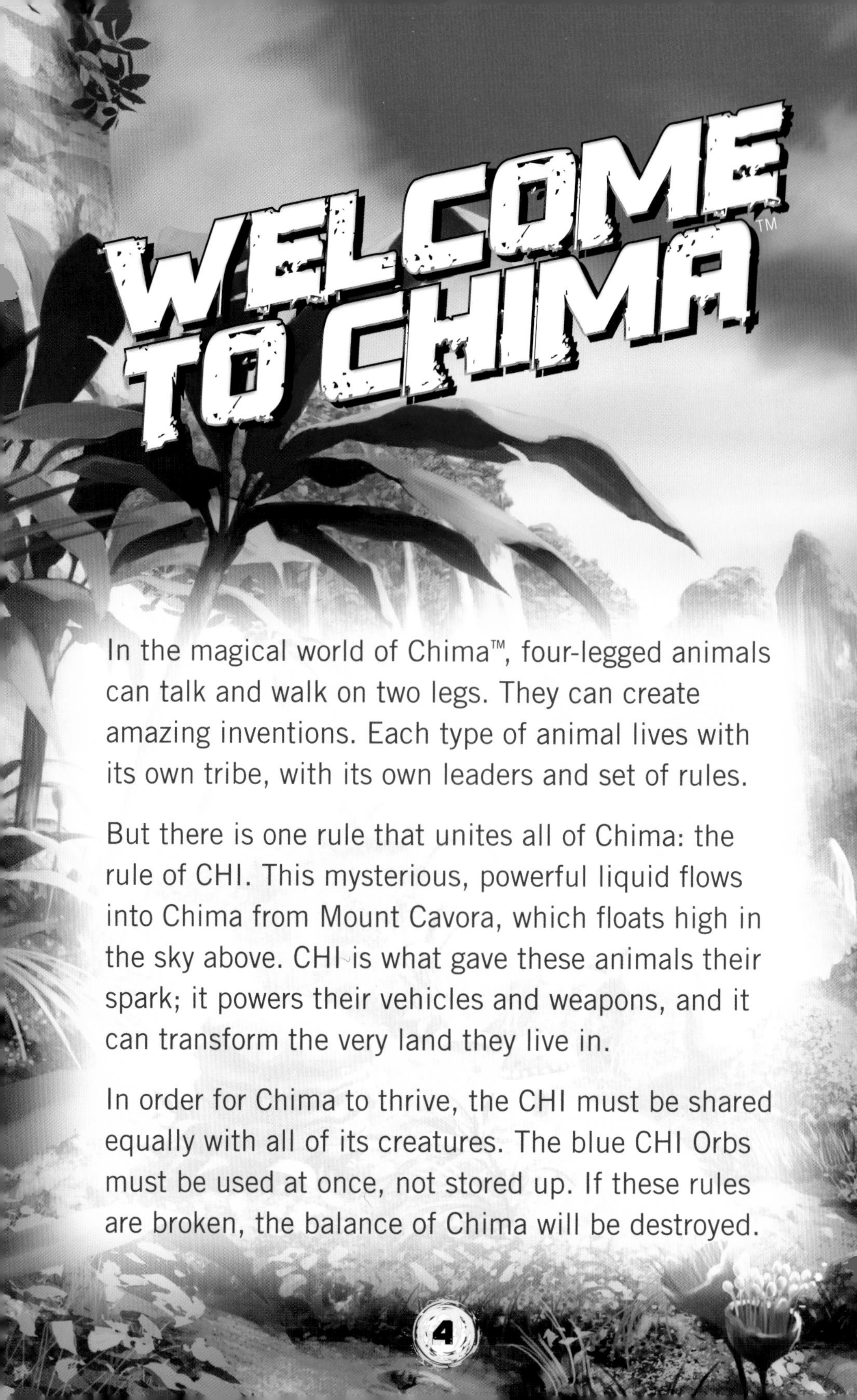

WELCOME TO CHIMA™

In the magical world of Chima™, four-legged animals can talk and walk on two legs. They can create amazing inventions. Each type of animal lives with its own tribe, with its own leaders and set of rules.

But there is one rule that unites all of Chima: the rule of CHI. This mysterious, powerful liquid flows into Chima from Mount Cavora, which floats high in the sky above. CHI is what gave these animals their spark; it powers their vehicles and weapons, and it can transform the very land they live in.

In order for Chima to thrive, the CHI must be shared equally with all of its creatures. The blue CHI Orbs must be used at once, not stored up. If these rules are broken, the balance of Chima will be destroyed.

Now that balance has been threatened. For centuries, the Lions have controlled the distribution of CHI fairly. But these days, the Crocodiles want the precious liquid for themselves. A battle has begun, and each tribe must pick a side.

The fight to save the land of Chima is filled with many stories, stories known as . . .

THE LEGENDS OF CHIMA.

THE LEGEND OF CHIMA

Long ago, Chima was a peaceful paradise. Rivers and streams flowed through green meadows and lush jungles. Birds soared across clear blue skies. Animals roamed the land, living in harmony with nature — and with one another.

A sudden bolt of lightning changed everything. A storm rocked the skies over Chima, pummeling the land with wind and rain. Then the lightning hit, making the ground shake and tremble. A swirling tornado snaked across the land, and a huge mountain rose from the broken earth and floated into the sky.

Magical waterfalls spilled from this floating mountain, filling a sacred pool with a powerful life-force called CHI. Curious, the four-legged beasts of the land approached the pool and drank. Birds swooped down from above and tasted the water.

One by one, the creatures began to change. Four-legged animals now walked on two legs. Birds could use their wings to grasp tools. These new, advanced animals could talk and plan and create. They formed tribes and quickly went to work, building new homes, vehicles, and weapons using the power of CHI.

Not all of the inhabitants of Chima drank from the pool, however. They feared these new advances would one day bring a dark cloud over their beloved land. These creatures slipped off into the Chima Outlands, never to be seen again. They became known as the Legend Beasts, and many in Chima doubt that they even exist.

Now Chima is in danger. A battle has begun between those who truly understand CHI and those who seek to control it for their own selfish purposes. It is time for the animals to choose sides . . . and for heroes to step up and save the world!

No one is sure where the mysterious liquid known as CHI came from. But over time, the inhabitants of Chima learned to use it to improve their lives.

CHI flows down from the waterfalls of Mount Cavora. It falls into a river and then gathers in the Sacred Pool. Because a Lion was first to drink from the CHI, members of the Lion Tribe guard the Sacred Pool.

The mystical waters of CHI mix with the minerals in the pool to form glowing blue CHI Orbs. Once a month, the orbs are harvested, and the Lions distribute them equally to the tribes. Over time, the tribes learned how to use the powers of CHI in some amazing ways.

The Lion Tribe must be sure to distribute the CHI equally. If there is ever too little or too much CHI in the Sacred Pool, Chima will suffer from earthquakes, storms, and other natural disasters.

WHAT IS CHI?

CHI UP!

When a youth in Chima reaches the Age of Becoming, he or she becomes a Chima Warrior. Each Chima Warrior is given a CHI harness. When an orb is placed in the harness, that warrior "powers up."

In a "CHI-up" moment, a glowing, oversize image of the warrior appears behind him or her, representing the power he/she feels inside. This surge of power can heighten a warrior's speed, strength, and instinct, and it may also bring to light hidden powers the warrior may have.

Sometimes a "CHI up" lasts for minutes, and other times it can last for hours. If the intention of the warrior using the CHI is good, the CHI will glow bright blue. If the warrior's intention is bad, the CHI will glow red.

A warrior must not use CHI before the Age of Becoming. The results could be harmful to the warrior — and all of Chima.

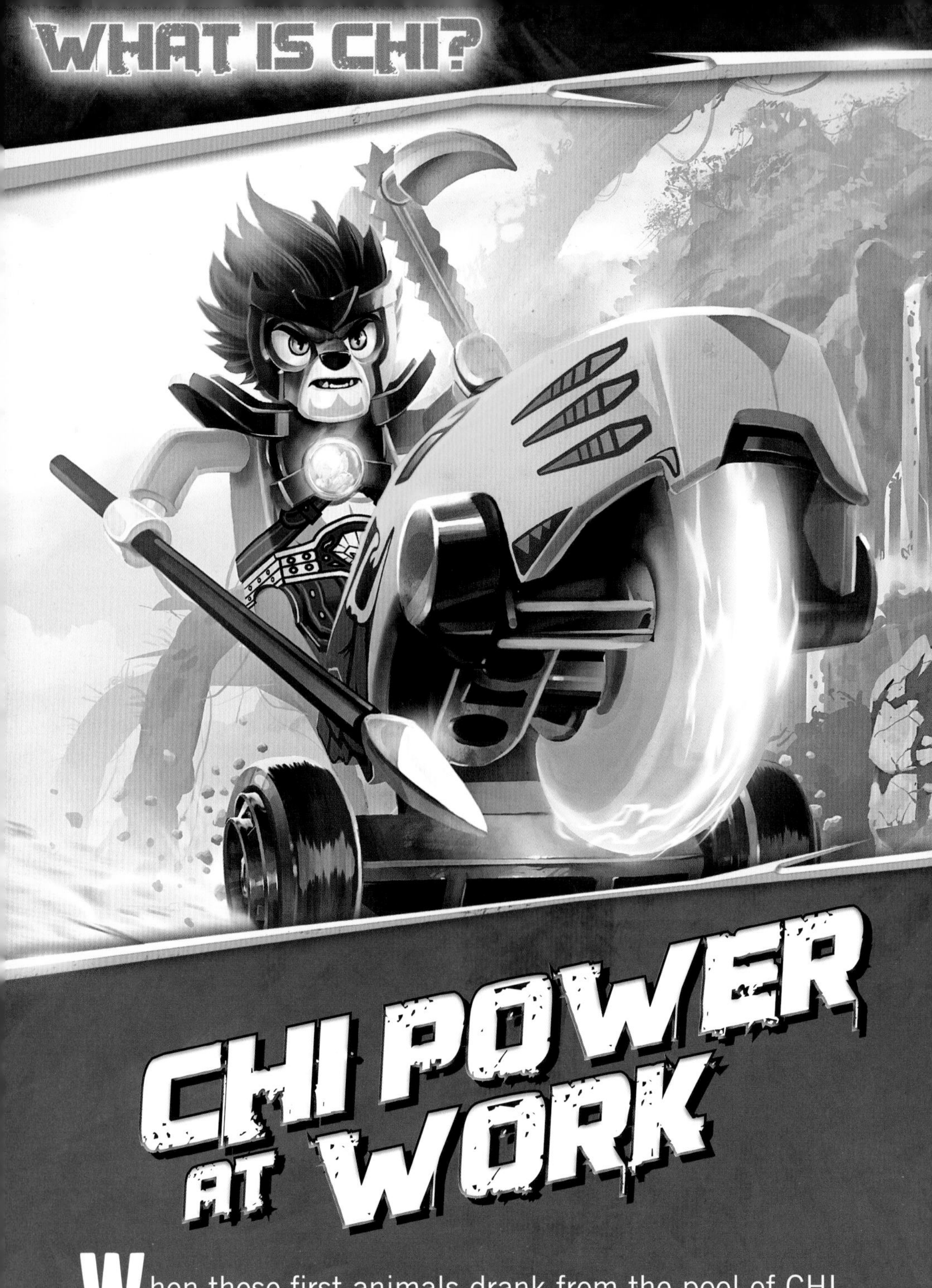

CHI POWER AT WORK

When those first animals drank from the pool of CHI, they experienced a burst of creative brainpower. They began to invent a vast array of CHI-powered machines.

First came the Speedor Wheels, and the Speedorz™ they powered. The wheels are carved from pieces of rock that fell from Mount Cavora the day it first appeared. These rocks are embedded with the powers of nature. When a CHI Orb is added to the wheel, it results in superspeed. Speedor Wheels are attached to chariots that are used for transportation, racing, and even battle.

As warriors created more sophisticated vehicles, such as planes, bikes, and battle machines, they used CHI Orbs to power them. Handheld weapons also use CHI power. If the weapon is being used for good, it will glow blue; a weapon being used for the wrong reason will glow red.

THE GOLDEN CHI

Each month, when the CHI Orbs are harvested, one special orb of Golden CHI is produced. Unlike regular CHI, Golden CHI never loses its power. It can be stored and used whenever necessary. Golden CHI also has the unique power to reshape landscapes and create elaborate structures from nothing.

As you can guess, every tribe wants the Golden CHI. To keep things fair, the Lions hold a monthly race for it. The winner of the race gets to keep the Golden CHI for their tribe.

Race day is an exciting day in Chima. Tribes come from all over to watch the races and shop in the marketplace that springs up every month. The most talented warrior in each tribe jumps on a Speedor and tries to win the race.

The Lions use the Golden CHI to create the racecourse each month. It's impossible to predict what kind of course the Golden CHI will form. Each course is completely different, but they all contain breathtaking twists, turns, and obstacles.

THE RACE IS ON!

"Get ready, race fans!" shouts Equila, the race-day announcer. "The CHI is choosing today's track. Will it be a test of speed? Agility? Or strength? Nobody knows."

Then the Lion Guards release the orb of Golden CHI, and everyone — spectators and racers alike — eagerly watches to see which challenge the orb will create. It could be any one of the following:

BOULDER BOWLING

Blast through boulders to free King Crominus from the trapped cave and return him to the Croc Tribe.

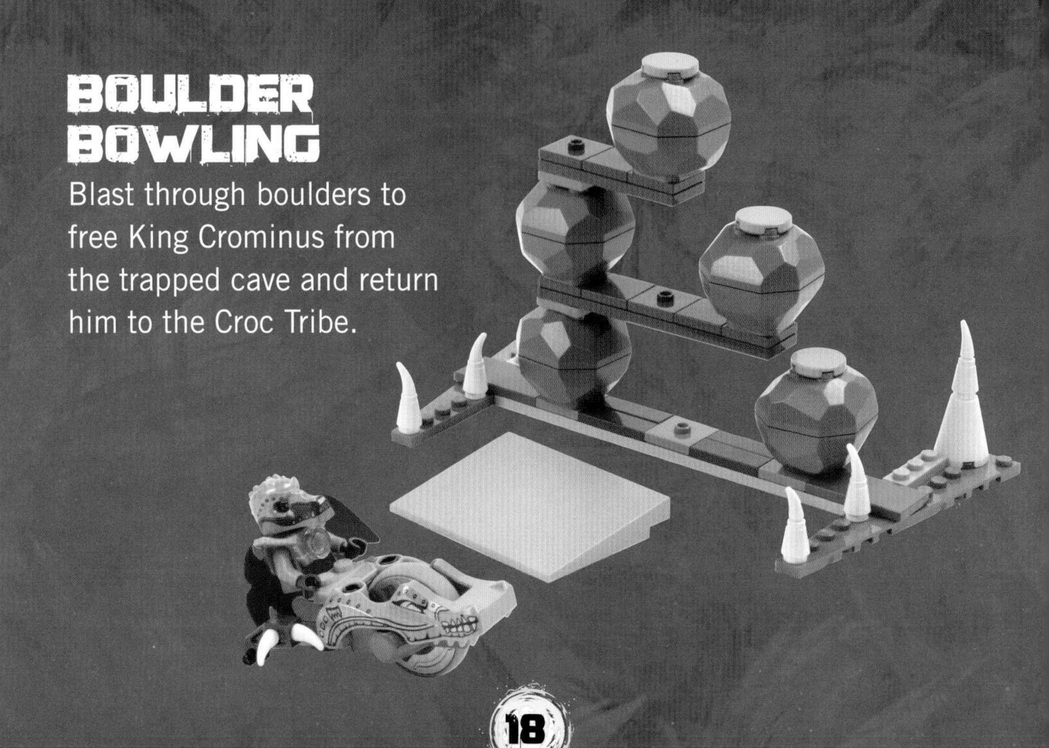

NEST DIVE

Soar high in the sky and land in the Eagle Nest to bring home the CHI.

CHI WATERFALL

Ride to the mystical CHI waterfall, hit the target, and catch the falling CHI.

TARGET PRACTICE

Soar through the aerial world of the Eagle Tribe and aim for the targets with your arrow.

RING OF FIRE

Race up the ramp and jump through the flaming hoop to win!

ICE TOWER

It takes speed and power to be the first to reach the ancient Ice Tower — and topple it!

JUNGLE GATES

Zoom through the leafy jungle and be the first to pass through the gates to take home the ultimate prize.

CHI BATTLES

Race up ramps and knock down targets to earn the prize.

EAGLES' CASTLE

Soar high in the skies over Chima and compete in an epic battle for the Golden CHI.

THE MAJOR TRIBES

When each new animal drank from the pool of CHI for the first time, the face of its kind was magically carved onto Mount Cavora. Each face represents one of the major tribes of Chima.

Each of these tribes is very different. They live in different environments and have different strengths and weaknesses. Some of the tribes, like the Lions, always work for good. Other tribes always seem to be up to no good, like the Ravens.

Although the tribes didn't always agree on everything, they managed to live together in harmony for years. But now the tide in Chima has turned, and close friends have become enemies as battles rage to decide who will control the CHI.

THE MAJOR TRIBES

To the members of the Lion Tribe, the law is everything. Because a Lion was the first to drink from the CHI, they believe it is their duty to guard the Sacred Pool, and they take it very seriously. They know that if the CHI is ever out of balance, Chima will suffer.

Lions stick to the rules, even if it's against their own best interests. If another tribe is causing them trouble, they will still make sure the troublesome tribe gets CHI during the monthly harvest.

Lions are also extremely loyal and brave. They live in stone temples and forts where the grasslands meet the jungles of Chima. They can expertly navigate the rocky territory on their Speedorz.

STRENGTHS: The Lions' sense of fairness and justice make them good leaders. They are also fierce competitors in the CHI races.

WEAKNESSES: The Lions forget that sometimes rules need to be broken.

LAGRAVIS

Laval's father is the king of the Lion Tribe, and is respected by his tribe members for his wisdom. Sometimes he can be stubborn and imperious about following tradition.

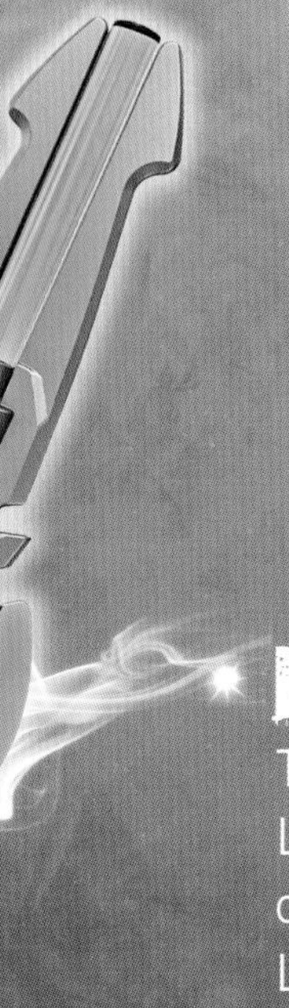

LAVAL

The son of LaGravis, Laval will rule his tribe one day. For more about Laval, turn to page 54.

LONGTOOTH

This seasoned Guardian of the Sacred Pool has many years of experience. He'd secretly love to retire, but when his tribe needs him, Longtooth will always be ready to fight.

LEONIDAS

Leonidas might not be the smartest Guardian of the Pool, but he's a hard worker who will complete any task he's given quickly and with skill.

LENNOX

This young Temple Guardian is brave and fast on his feet. He is always ready to battle for his tribe.

THE
LION CHI
TEMPLE

The members of the Lion Tribe live in ancient stone forts surrounding the Lion CHI Temple, which holds the Sacred Pool of CHI. The Temple is fortified with several defensive features:

- a watchtower equipped with CHI-powered weapons
- a drawbridge with a gate
- two hidden Lion Claw Racers

All of these features were designed by the Lions to protect the precious CHI inside the Temple.

THE MAJOR TRIBES

To find the Crocodile Tribe, you'll have to venture into the murky swamps of Chima. Crocs can live both in water and on land, so they thrive in this environment.

Crocs are known for being slippery and sneaky — you can't fully trust them. In battle, they fight fiercely with weapons that resemble their own sharp fangs. Their armorlike skin protects them from danger.

For centuries, the Crocs followed the Code of Chima. They forged friendships with the Lions, even though they didn't like all of the Lions' rules. But now that all has changed, and these two tribes are at the forefront of the battle for CHI.

STRENGTHS: Clever and adaptable, Crocs can find an advantage on almost any battlefield.

WEAKNESSES: They are so consumed with winning, they sometimes lose sight of what they're fighting for.

CROMINUS

The former king of the Crocodile Tribe has gone missing. This levelheaded leader kept the Crocs out of trouble for many years.

The son of Crominus and new leader of the Crocodile Tribe, Cragger is more competitive than his father. For more details about Cragger, turn to page 56.

CROOLER

Cragger's sister is ambitious and hungry for power. She tries to get what she wants by making Cragger take all the risks, while she reaps the reward.

CRUG

Crug is Cragger's number-one thug. Big and strong, he'll do whatever Cragger orders. He might be unpredictable and dangerous, but he has a softer side, too — he sleeps with a stuffed frog he calls "Mr. FlipperLovey."

CRAWLEY

Cragger's second-in-command, Crawley is nervous and quick. He uses his tail like a super-powered whip, tripping or pounding his opponents as he lashes out at them.

THE CROC SWAMP HIDEOUT

The dwelling of the Crocodiles is hidden inside the swamps of Chima. Any intruders looking to steal the Crocs' Golden CHI need to be on the lookout for traps and hazards:

- A snapping gate shaped like a Croc Jaw protects the Golden CHI
- Croc Guards operate rocket shooters
- A hanging prison cell awaits any intruders who get caught
- The Crocs constantly forge new weapons in their workshop

THE MAJOR TRIBES

Don't bother bringing your Speedor if you visit the Eagles. They live in dwellings high in the rocky cliffs overlooking Chima. There are no roads or bridges, because they fly anywhere they need to go.

Maybe it's because they live in the clouds, but Eagles can get a little spacey sometimes. Eagles are very intelligent, but it's easy for them to get lost in their own thoughts. They love to read and research, and they can talk for hours about a new idea or favorite subject.

Don't underestimate the Eagles in battle. It's difficult to defend against their swift and punishing aerial attacks, and they're great strategists, too.

STRENGTHS: Observant and wise, Eagles often know the best solution to a problem.

WEAKNESSES: Eagles can be "airheads" who lose focus in the heat of the moment.

EWALD

This wise Eagle was elected by his tribe to lead the Eagles' Ruling Council. He will debate for hours or even days to find the solution to a problem — although sometimes that means that when he finally makes up his mind, it's too late.

ERIS

The daughter of a member of the Ruling Council, Eris is also a good friend of Laval's. She has a sense of adventure that's unusual in the Eagle Tribe. For more information, turn to page 58.

EQUILA

Equila is one of the fastest and most agile flyers in all of Chima — and his mouth is almost as fast as his wings! That's why he's a natural as the announcer for the monthly CHI-Day races.

EGLOR

The "gadget-bird" of the Eagle Tribe, Eglor is a master of weapons and rocketry. When he finishes his inventions on time, the Eagles' enemies are in trouble. But often, the fight is over before this absentminded genius is finished.

EWAR

Ewar is one of the strongest and most powerful warriors in the Eagle Tribe. He is respected by the other Eagles for his wisdom and judgment in battle.

THE MAJOR TRIBES

To the members of the Wolf Tribe, it's all about the pack. When it's time to take sides in a battle, they'll make sure to look out for their own survival before any other cause or allegiance. The survival of the pack is their number-one priority.

Wolves like to stick close together. They live in weapons-equipped vehicles and are always on the move. They'll sleep in tightly packed piles so they can cram as many warriors into each vehicle as possible.

Wolves can be sneaky, and they can disguise their vehicles to blend in with the environment around them. Any opponent who stumbles upon one of their hidden lairs by mistake had better run from these ferocious fighters.

STRENGTHS: A pack that works well together can come through almost any dangerous situation.

WEAKNESSES: Their instinct for self-preservation can make them appear cowardly.

WORRIZ

When the animal tribes meet, Worriz represents the Wolf Tribe. For more about Worriz, turn to page 60.

WINZAR

Young and reckless, Winzar will often pick a fight to try to impress the older Wolves. His inexperience can get him into big trouble.

WAKZ

The oldest and most experienced member of the tribe, you'll often find Wakz operating a cannon during battle.

WILHURT

Dark and dangerous, Wilhurt is the meanest fighter and hunter in the tribe. When he's not hunting or fighting, he can get a little wild, so it's best to keep him occupied.

WINDRA

She might have the whitest fur in the tribe, but Windra also has the blackest heart. Cold and ruthless, she's all snapping jaws and swiping claws on the battlefield.

THE MAJOR TRIBES

Gorillas are probably the strongest warriors in Chima. They're also the most peaceful — they'll only fight if it's absolutely necessary.

The Gorilla Tribe lives in the lush green jungles of Chima, where they enjoy the beauty of nature and try to become one with "the Great Mellow." Not much bothers the Gorillas. Their motto is "live and let live."

But when the tribe is in danger, or the fate of Chima hangs in the balance, the Gorillas will take action — and when they do, look out! Besides being amazingly powerful, they're also incredibly agile — a devastating combination.

STRENGTHS: **Incredible physical power and agility, plus the ability to remain calm during a crisis.**

WEAKNESSES: **Their peaceful nature means that sometimes the bad guys can take advantage of them.**

GRUMLO

The Gorillas don't have a king, but Grumlo is their spiritual leader. He leads the daily yoga sessions and teaches the tribe how to meditate. All that yoga means that Grumlo is a skilled athlete who is always one step ahead of his enemy.

GORZAN

Gorzan is one of the strongest fighters in his tribe, and his emotions are just as strong as he is. For more about Gorzan, go to page 64.

GRIZZAM

Grizzam is the only white-furred Gorilla. His unusual fur has always made him feel different from the rest of the Tribe, but like the other Gorillas, he is mellow to the core.

G'LOONA

G'loona is a sweet, young orphan who looks up to Gorzan like a big brother. She wants to help Gorzan and Eris on all their missions, but her youth and inexperience often get her in trouble. Fortunately, Gorzan is usually there to bail her out.

THE MAJOR TRIBES

All the members of the Raven Tribe are thieves — it's in their nature. They'll steal the Speedor from right underneath you, and then offer to sell it back to you. They don't care if an item is valuable or not. If it's there, they'll take it.

This endless urge to steal means that the Ravens have quite the crazy collection of objects, and they use them to create their Nest Forts, which can go on for miles. Intruders often get lost in the messy maze — usually under silly circumstances.

When it's time to choose sides in a conflict, Ravens aren't interested in who's right and who's wrong. They'll fight for whomever pays them the most. During battle, they keep their eyes open for chances to snitch treasure. In fact, their opponents are sometimes glad the Ravens chose the other side!

STRENGTHS: Their clever tongues mean that they can easily fool or trick others.

WEAKNESSES: When you don't care who you trick, you make a lot of enemies.

MEET THE RAVENS

RAWZOM

The unofficial king of the Raven Tribe, Rawzom is a natural schemer. He always puts the tribe first.

RAZAR

Razar is the slickest talker in the whole Raven tribe. To find out more about him, turn to page 62.

RAZCAL

A tribe as obsessed with money as the Ravens needs an accountant, and that's Razcal. The Ravens are always in competition with one another to see who's the best thief, so Razcal's accounts are important to them.

RIZZO

This scruffy scavenger sports an eye patch and a peg leg, much like a pirate. He's the bottom of the bottom-feeders, and he wears that badge with pride.

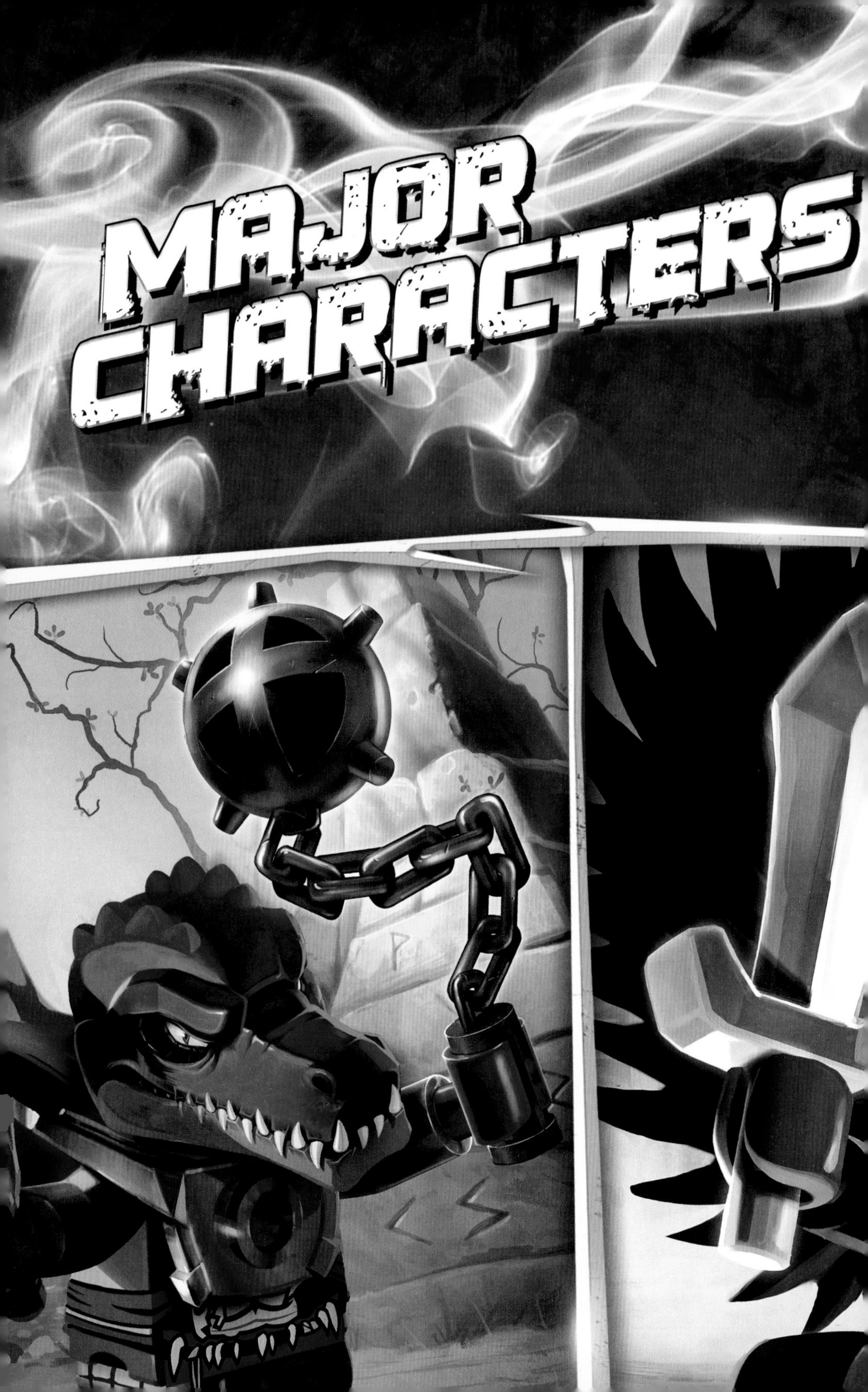
MAJOR
CHARACTERS

After centuries of living in peace, Chima's tribes are now battling for control of the precious CHI. Each tribe member plays an important role in the battle. The decisions they make will determine whether Chima thrives — or is lost forever.

MAJOR CHARACTERS

LAVAL THE LION

It's not always easy growing up in a tribe where rules are the most important thing — especially for a mischievous young Lion like Laval. He's playful at heart, and loves to pull pranks. As you can imagine, this got him into trouble a lot when he was a kid.

Now that Laval is older, he's more mature. Protecting Chima is his goal, and he'll bravely venture into dangerous situations to achieve it. He still has a sense of adventure and loves to have fun, and these qualities will help him become the great warrior he is destined to be.

BEST FRIEND: Eris

WEAPON: Royal Valious, his sword

FIGHTING STYLE: Laval is master of the crushing Lion Pounce.

HOBBIES: Racing his Speedor across the rocky plains of Chima

DISLIKES: Water (He's not a great swimmer.)

QUOTE: "For the tribes — and for Chima! C'mon . . . it'll be fun!"

MAJOR CHARACTERS

When he was a young Croc, Cragger was best friends with Laval. The two of them eagerly explored Chima, competing in games like hide-and-seek.

Then, one day, Cragger's curious nature got him into trouble when he harnessed the power of a CHI Orb before he was ready to handle it. Cragger spiraled out of control, the Lions tried to stop him, and a series of misunderstandings soon led to battle between the Lions and the Crocs.

Cragger and Laval aren't friends anymore. Now all Cragger wants is for the Crocodile Tribe to gain control of the CHI — no matter what the cost.

NEW BEST FRIEND: Worriz

WEAPON: Vengdualize, a snaggletoothed CHI Spear

FIGHTING STYLE: Aggressive; he doesn't have any defensive moves.

HOBBIES: Sneaking into places he doesn't belong

DISLIKES: Losing

QUOTE: "No mercy. Ever. Really. I mean it."

MAJOR CHARACTERS

ERIS THE EAGLE

Laval knows that he can always count on his new best friend, Eris. She's loyal, kind, brave, and will always lend a hand when it's needed.

In battle, Eris fights with her brain. She's a great strategist and she can always calculate the right time to make the best move. When Eris flies through the sky in her Eagle Interceptor, she almost always hits her target.

Like the other Eagles, Eris loves books and storytelling, but she's not as much of an airhead as her other tribe members. That might be why she gets along so well with earthbound warriors like Laval. Her levelheadedness makes the other Eagles think she's a little odd.

BEST FRIEND: Laval

WEAPON: Eglaxxor, her golden CHI-powered axe

FIGHTING STYLE: Swoops down from the sky to strike, strike, and strike again

HOBBIES: Telling jokes and stories

DISLIKES: Animals who want to fight instead of talk

QUOTE: "It's not just the noble thing to do. It's the *right* thing to do."

MAJOR CHARACTERS

WORRIZ THE WOLF

Members of the Wolf Tribe travel in packs and make group decisions easily, so they don't have a leader or a king. But they do need someone to represent them when they deal with other tribes, and that Wolf is Worriz.

Worriz got the job because he is the best at pretending he's friendly. He can disguise his vicious, cruel nature long enough to negotiate with others to get what the tribe wants or needs. But when the negotiation is over, watch out! Worriz has sharp claws and even sharper fangs, and he's not afraid to use them.

BEST FRIEND: Cragger (although Worriz can't wait to overthrow him and take his place)

WEAPON: Maulus, his CHI-powered weapon

FIGHTING STYLE: Ruthless and unstoppable

HOBBIES: Hanging with his Wolf Pack

DISLIKES: Talking about his feelings

QUOTE: "We fight as one, and we think as one. When we put our minds together, we can do anything."

In the battle for Chima, some are in it for honor, some are in it for control, and Razar is in it for greed. He wants to become the richest creature in Chima, and he'll do whatever it takes to achieve his goal. He has aligned himself with Cragger because he thinks that's the most profitable path, but he would change sides in a heartbeat if he thought he could gain from it.

If Razar is ever generous, be suspicious. He's probably up to something. Razar won't ever do the right thing unless he's being paid for it. He'll fight for whichever side will pay him the most — and then steal their weapons when they're not looking.

BEST FRIEND: None, but he hangs out with Razcal and Rizzo

WEAPON: Thundax, his forked spear

FIGHTING STYLE: He's slippery, and he'll run away if there's no gain in it for him.

HOBBIES: Wheeling, dealing, and stealing

DISLIKES: Working for free

QUOTE: "I'll make you a deal."

MAJOR CHARACTERS

Like the other Gorillas, Gorzan is a sensitive soul. He's happiest hanging out in the jungles of Chima, eating fruit and tending to the flowers.

But when the things Gorzan loves are threatened, he becomes a wildly powerful fighter. No other warrior can match his strength, and his agility makes him doubly dangerous. When Gorzan climbs into his Gorilla Striker, a giant Gorilla Robot Suit, there's no stopping him.

When the fighting is over, Gorzan will be sad about the flowers he's stomped on and the damage he's caused. This peaceful warrior would much rather chill than fight.

BEST FRIEND: **Anyone who says "hi" to him**

WEAPON: **Cudgellor, his fist-hammer**

FIGHTING STYLE: **Pounding, pummeling, and stomping**

HOBBIES: **Smelling flowers, watching rainbows**

DISLIKES: **Those who try to mess with this beautiful world we live in**

QUOTE: ***"Duuude!"***

MAJOR CHARACTERS

Hatched just seconds after her twin brother, Cragger, Crooler is the princess of the Crocodile Tribe. When their parents went missing, Cragger, the eldest child, became the new king. This made Crooler seethe with jealousy — but then she quickly saw the advantage in the situation.

Crooler realized she could control the tribe through Cragger without having to get her hands dirty. She pushes his buttons and pulls his strings, getting him to do what she wants. If things go wrong, Cragger gets the blame. If they succeed, Crooler is one step closer to controlling the CHI for herself.

FORMER BEST FRIEND: Eris. These supersmart girls were close until Crooler became obsessed with gaining power.

FIGHTING STYLE: Crooler would rather get someone else to do the dirty work for her.

HOBBIES: Manipulating others

DISLIKES: The way everyone looks up to those "high and mighty" Lions

QUOTE: "I'm not mean. You're just weak."

SKINNET THE SKUNK

Skinnet is always trying to get close to the action, and he would love to be a hero some day. But whenever he enters a situation, everyone scatters, and Skinnet loses his chance.

It's all because of Skinnet's smelly Skunk Powers, which he can't control. His powerful stench usually slips out at exactly the wrong time. This means that Skinnet is usually on his own; the other members of his tribe have long vanished.

The warrior closest to Skinnet is Eris the Eagle, who is always nice to him. But maybe that's because she can fly away when things get stinky!

BEST FRIEND: **Poor Skinnet! Nobody wants to get close enough to him to be his best friend.**

WEAPON: **Stynkjahak, a spear with smelly surprises**

FIGHTING STYLE: **Stinky**

HOBBIES: **Finding out where the action is so he can join in**

DISLIKES: **That everyone runs away from him**

QUOTE: ***"Sorrrry!"***

MAJOR CHARACTERS

Furty the Fox is one of Chima's most cunning animals. He is said to be related to the Wolves, but he couldn't be more different from them. Furty's a loner. Orphaned at an early age, he quickly learned to take care of number one.

Despite his self-centered nature, Furty seems so innocent that he's easily able to convince others to do as he wishes. He just gives them a little nudge in the right direction . . . and lets them do the rest. If he's found out, he's almost always forgiven — there's something so harmless about him that the other animals just can't stay mad.

BEST FRIEND: None. Furty prefers to fly solo.

WEAPON: CHI Whippa, a spiky CHI Whip

FIGHTING STYLE: Sly like a fox

HOBBIES: Blending into a big crowd . . . so he can make mischief

DISLIKES: Getting caught making mischief

QUOTE: "Confusion, mistrust, deception. That's my specialty!"

MAJOR CHARACTERS

THE LEGEND BEASTS

They're called "Legend Beasts" because for centuries, no one was sure if they actually existed. According to the story, these creatures left Chima a thousand years ago, after refusing to drink from the pool of CHI. They did not change and remained in their original animal forms.

Laval was the first one to encounter a Legend Beast, a Lion who appeared to be on the side of good. Whether there are more Legend Beasts — and if they will help decide the fate of Chima — remains to be seen.

VEHICLES

Each tribe has created vehicles custom-built to play up that tribe's special strengths. But all vehicles in Chima have one thing in common: the awesome power of CHI.

LAVAL'S ROYAL FIGHTER

Lions are built for making their way across rough terrain, and Laval's vehicle takes that ability to the max. Four big tracks power this Fighter across jagged rocks and bumpy ground, which means that Laval can follow an opponent just about anywhere.

The body of this Fighter is a mechanical Lion's Head with jaws that move up and down to take a bite out of anyone who gets too close. A CHI-powered cannon allows the operator to take aim at long-distance targets.

When Laval powers up the Fighter, he'll let trusted guard Longtooth do the driving while he takes his position in the cannon tower.

WEAPONS: Cannon, biting mouth

CREW: 2

CHI FEATURES: CHI-powered motor and cannon

SPECIAL EQUIPMENT: Tracks and mission map

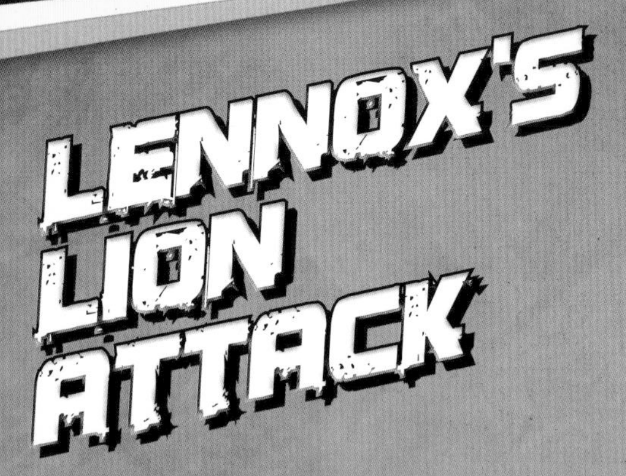

This energetic young Lion Guard pilots a vehicle that's like an extension of his powerful body. The Lion Attack is the perfect combination of Lion and machine: It has the speed and sharp claws of a Lion, with the added ability to shoot projectile weapons.

The Lion Attack is designed for close combat as well as distance fighting. The claws extending from the front wheels are the ultimate defensive feature. And Lennox can shoot discs right from the open mouth of the Lion's Head.

If you see Lennox's Lion Attack coming toward you, have no fear. You can tell by the blue glow in the Lion's Eyes that Lennox is fighting for the good of Chima.

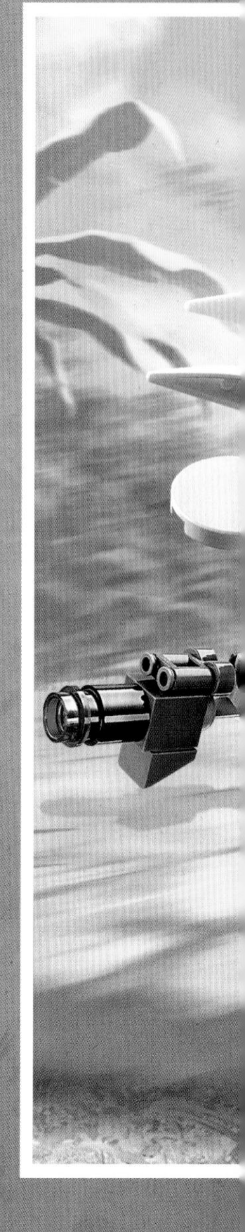

WEAPONS: Rapid disc shooter, claws, flicker missiles

CREW: 1

CHI FEATURES: CHI-powered claws and engine

SPECIAL EQUIPMENT: Strong rubber wheels

ERIS'S EAGLE INTERCEPTOR

Imagine you're on the ground and you hear the loud roar of an engine in the sky above. You look up — and see this massive mechanical Eagle speeding toward you!

Eris's fighter plane is designed like a fully functional Eagle. Movable wings and tail steer the fighter through strong currents. Sharp claws add offensive power to the landing gear.

The Eagle Head, with its fierce, yellow beak, intimidates opponents while holding the pilot inside. In an emergency, the head can eject and the pilot can fly to safety. But it will take a lot to separate Eris from her plane. She has to protect the CHI stored in the box in the back.

WEAPONS: Eagle Flicker Missles and sharp grabbing claws

CREW: 1

CHI FEATURES: CHI-powered engine

SPECIAL EQUIPMENT: Surprise eject function

EGLOR'S TWIN BIKE

Eagles are hard to beat in an aerial battle, but they can be at a disadvantage on the ground. So Eglor, the Eagle Tribe's main inventor, came up with this ingenious vehicle that functions both on land *and* in the air.

On the ground, big all-terrain wheels allow the Twin Bike to travel across different kinds of landscapes. The wheels are powered by CHI, which gives the bike an extra boost.

Then, with a touch of a button, the bike can convert into an Eagle Jet with movable wings and tail. So if things get tough on the ground, Eglor can take to the skies.

WEAPONS: Wing Blasters

CREW: 1

CHI FEATURES: CHI-powered wheels

SPECIAL EQUIPMENT: All-terrain tires

EQUILA'S ULTRA STRIKER

Another invention of Eglor's, Equila's Ultra Striker is the ultimate land vehicle in the Eagle Tribe's battle arsenal. Its massive size and huge treads means it can venture just about anywhere in Chima.

The body of the Ultra Striker resembles an Eagle with jagged tail feathers and sharp claws in front. The cockpit can eject and fly on its own, so the warriors inside can take the battle to the sky.

Eglor built the Ultra Striker for Equila, one of the Eagle Tribe's top warriors. Equila tested the vehicle in a skirmish against the Wolves, and the Eagles were victorious. The Eagles are lucky to have an inventor like Eglor on their side.

WEAPONS: Eagle Rocket Shooters

CREW: 2

CHI FEATURES: CHI-powered engine under each wing

SPECIAL EQUIPMENT: Big rubber tracks

GORZAN'S GORILLA STRIKER

What's that stomping through the jungle? Is it a giant Gorilla? No, it's Gorzan in his incredible battle machine!

This machine is a big, powerful robot that looks like a Gorilla. Gorzan sits inside and controls the movements of the Striker's arms, hands, legs, and weapons. The vehicle moves with the same agility and speed of a Gorilla — except it's ten times bigger!

Strong blue CHI flows through the power cables, giving an extra boost of energy to all the robot's functions. Gorzan can smash and bash obstacles with the big arms while shooting out both CHI-powered missiles and bananas. There's no stopping Gorzan when he's in his Gorilla Striker!

WEAPONS: **CHI missiles and Banana Shooter**

CREW: **1**

CHI FEATURES: **CHI-powered cables**

SPECIAL EQUIPMENT: **Swinging arms and articulated hands**

CRAGGER'S COMMAND SHIP

The crowning vehicle of the Crocodile Tribe, Cragger's Command Ship rules the rivers of Chima. CHI powers this ship as it travels through the waters, its Crocodile Tail thrashing behind it.

The front of the ship looks like the fierce head of a Crocodile, with eyes that glow red with CHI. The eyes are cockpits that can hold one pilot each.

In battle, the Ship's jaws snap up and down, revealing sharp fangs. From his position inside the cockpit, Cragger can shoot flicker missiles at his enemies. If he needs to change the direction of the battle, Cragger can take to the air in the hidden Croc Helicopter, or send out his warriors in two Croc Mini-Boats.

WEAPONS: Flicker missiles and a mouth of ultra-sharp teeth

CREW: 3

CHI FEATURES: Hidden CHI-powered engine

SPECIAL EQUIPMENT: Snapping mouth opens wide to hold crew and prisoners

CRAWLEY'S CLAW RIPPER

This Croc Vehicle is specially designed for its swamp habitat. In the back, the oversized rear wheels are made to power it through the thickest muck and mud. In the front, biting jaws can trap an enemy inside.

The most awesome feature of Crawley's Claw Ripper might be the spinning claws attached to the front treads. They'll ferociously tear through anything they encounter.

Because the Crocodiles are determined to get CHI any way they can, this vehicle has a hidden compartment for storing stolen CHI. If the Lions want to get the CHI back, they'll have to get past the Claw Ripper's spinning claws!

WEAPONS: Biting mouth and ripping claws

CREW: 1

CHI FEATURES: Secret CHI chest

SPECIAL EQUIPMENT: Extra-large rear wheels

VEHICLES

WEAPONS: Five CHI-powered weapons and one standard weapon

CREW: 4

CHI FEATURES: CHI-powered weapons and motor

SPECIAL EQUIPMENT: Six extra-large wheels and a mobile prison

Worriz's Combat Lair

It's a Wolf Den! It's a vehicle! It's both! Worriz's Combat Lair can function as one high-powered battle machine or separate into five different modules.

Worriz can press sliders to deploy Claw Bikes that can send two warriors racing into battle. He can take flight in a Wolf Helicopter if he needs to face the Eagles in an aerial fight. A mobile prison detaches, ready to hold any prisoners. And there's an extra motorbike in the back if Worriz needs to make a quick getaway.

Even after all those features are deployed, Worriz is left with a CHI-powered vehicle that can travel across any terrain. It's like having five vehicles in one, with something for every Wolf in the pack.

WAKZ'S PACK TRACKER

Wolves are expert trackers, and they've created a vehicle that helps them track opponents in a variety of environments. The Pack Tracker's all-terrain wheels can handle Chima's murky swamps as well as its rocky ridges. From his perch in the driver's seat, Wakz can keep an eye on his Eagle enemies in the sky.

The Pack Tracker's design is meant to intimidate. The body looks like a ferocious Wolf Head with snapping jaws, and pointy teeth protrude from the wheels. A long-range shooter that the driver operates brings force to the Tracker's frightening appearance. The chain winch is the final touch—its claws are designed to capture Eagles as they flee through the air.

There might not be enough room for a whole Wolf Pack on this Tracker, but it does hold two drivers, a prisoner, and a store of CHI.

WEAPONS: Wolf Shooter

CREW: 2

CHI FEATURES: Jaws that snap as Wakz drives

SPECIAL EQUIPMENT: Working winch, off-road suspension

RAZAR'S CHI RAIDER

Razar loves to soar across the skies in his CHI Raider, searching for precious CHI or anything else he can steal. There's plenty of storage in the back to hold his treasures and even a crew member or two.

This aggressive-looking flier resembles a Raven with a dark black body, purple wings, and glowing red accents.

If Razar needs to protect his spoils, he can launch an offensive missile attack. Or he could fly away to safety — and search for something else to steal.

WEAPONS: Flicker missiles

CREW: 2

CHI FEATURES: CHI-powered engine

SPECIAL EQUIPMENT: Movable wings, tail, and feet

RAZCAL'S GLIDER

The CHI powering this Glider enables it to fly through the sky faster than any bird. Razcal's Glider looks like a sleek, black Raven with a sharp beak, and it packs some ingenious surprises.

Razcal can lower a chain with a handle on the end so that he can scoop up things on the ground — CHI Orbs, treasures, even opponents. He can also fly low to the ground and pick up objects with the plane's landing legs.

The smaller size of the Glider is an advantage, too. Razcal can fly alongside Razar's CHI Raider so they can work as a team, or he can charge down from the skies to surprise opponents hiding out in tight spots.

WEAPONS: Push-out chain

CREW: 1

CHI FEATURES: CHI-powered engine

SPECIAL EQUIPMENT: Landing legs

LOCATIONS

Chima is a magical land, home to raging rivers, rocky cliffs, plant-filled jungles, and murky swamps. No matter where you visit, something exciting is always happening.

MOUNT CAVORA

Mount Cavora — the source of CHI — floats majestically in the center of Chima. Its sides are enormous rocks carved in the shape of Chima's eight great animal tribes. The carvings appeared when the first animals drank from the CHI waters.

Mount Cavora can be seen all over Chima, but no one has ever explored it. That's because the same powerful force that keeps the mountain suspended in mid-air also keeps Eagles and other flying creatures off its slopes. Legend has it that anyone who sets foot on Mount Cavora will immediately burst into flames.

THE CHI-DAY MARKET

Once a month, the Lions hold a race to see which tribe will get the precious orb of Golden CHI. Every resident of Chima flocks to see the exciting Speedor races. The Ravens, who never miss an opportunity to profit, started the CHI-Day Market that is held every racing day.

The market is filled with stalls run by members of every tribe, who sell everything from food to weapons to vehicle parts. Things can get chaotic and rowdy as bargains are made and salesmen compete to be the loudest to hawk their wares. But mostly it's a fun and exciting experience.

THE FANGS

This is a plain of petrified rock that looks like a huge beast with fangs sticking up from the ground. Was the beast real at one time? Nobody knows for sure. Navigating the Fangs can be treacherous. The Lions are the only creatures who even go near it, and they've become expert at racing their Speedorz across the obstacle-filled plateau.

THE OUTLANDS

Even the bravest warriors in Chima shiver at the thought of crossing over into the Outlands. This dark and twisting jungle is shrouded in mist, mystery, and danger. Traveling there has been forbidden for centuries.

That doesn't mean that the Outlands are uninhabited. It is believed that the Legend Beasts retreated to the Outlands after Mount Cavora appeared. Warriors who break the rules have been banished to the Outlands as well.

Perhaps the most dangerous inhabitant of the Outlands isn't an animal — it's a plant! The Predator Plant evolved after small amounts of CHI flowed into the wilderness through underground springs. The plant's limbs can attack, and its roots can crawl and seek out prey. Just one more reason to steer clear of the Outlands!

THE FALLING JUNGLE

The trees in this jungle don't grow straight up: They grow sideways and even downward! This makes it look like the trees are about to fall over, but they're really superstrong. Their thick roots can extend from one side of Chima to another, giving the trees awesome stability.

These amazing roots stick out of the ground, which makes traveling through the Falling Jungle tricky. Delicious fruits grow from the roots, but think twice before you pick one — picking a fruit can cause a tree to fall down elsewhere in the jungle.

THE GORGE OF ETERNAL DEPTH

If you're walking near the edge of the Fangs, be careful. If you don't watch your step, you may fall into the Gorge of Eternal Depth, a ravine so deep that nobody is sure if it has a bottom. If you listen closely, you will hear strange sounds emanating from the depths.

Cragger's parents, King Crominus and Queen Crunket, fell into this dark abyss in the heat of battle. Cragger is sure they are gone forever, but the Gorge of Eternal Depth holds many secrets . . . and surprises.

FOREVER ROCK

The youngest animals in Chima gravitate toward this big, smooth rock, which is great for climbing and the perfect setting for all kinds of adventure games. When Laval and Cragger were growing up, they kept track of their hide-and-seek matches by carving tally marks on the rock. The rock is covered with marks made by other kids. Forever Rock is the home of happy memories for many creatures.

SHADOW HILLS

A valley in the Chima countryside is always shrouded in shadows cast by these hills, which are shaped like the original animals that inhabited Chima. Making your way along the twisting and turning roads that traverse the hills can be a real challenge, which makes this an excellent setting for a Speedor race. Only the most skilled riders can conquer this course.

Using the power of CHI, Chima's inventors create weapons that are unique to each tribe.

LAVAL'S ROYAL VALIOUS SWORD

Laval's sword is one of the first ancient weapons of honor forged in Chima. It has been passed down through generations, and it is said to enlighten and protect its bearer. Only the bravest and most loyal protectors of Chima can wield it.

CRAGGER'S VENGDUALIZE SPEAR

One of Cragger's favorite weapons, Vengdualize, looks like a primitive collection of Crocodile teeth on a long stick, but it's boosted by technology. A small interior motor spins the blades like a chain saw.

RAZAR'S THUNDAX CHI SPEAR

Thundax is a scrap-metal invention with a clever paint job. Razar claims the blue blades are Raven wings. It fires an ear-splitting, CHI-powered shriek that leaves the enemy's ears ringing for days.

WORRIZ'S DOUBLE-FANGED CHI STAFF, MAULUS

This weapon's white fangs are a tribute to the Mother Wolf, who blessed all Wolves with their powers. Having two fangs in one weapon is the mark of the Wolf — they think and strike as one.

FURTY'S CHI WHIPPA

Furty loves his CHI Whippa. He's not sure exactly how to make the most of its CHI powers, but that's okay. Furty will never tell you how or where he got the Whippa, so whatever the deal was, odds are it probably wasn't legal.

GORZAN'S CUDGELLOR FIST HAMMER

Gorillas crave simple tools for their big hands. The Cudgellor was originally used for back scratching. It has since proven itself useful for plunging through shrubbery or poking fruit from trees. In battle, the size and weight of the Cudgellor more than make up for its unsophisticated design.

SKINNET'S STYNKJAHAK SPEAR

The Stynkjahak is Skinnet's pride, joy, and favorite toy. He hates the idea of harming others, so he decorated this jahak and uses it as a walking stick. For good measure, Skinnet added his best Skunk Scent and turned it into a weapon of gas destruction.

To truly understand the conflict over CHI, you must enter the world of Chima. In this story, Cragger gets close to his goal of gaining control over CHI — and Laval and Eris must race to stop him.

Laval pushed the broom back and forth across the stone floor, grumbling.

"Hey, Laval. Why so glum?" asked his friend Eris, entering the map room.

"Gotta clean up in here," the young Lion complained. "My dad says a great leader needs to understand the value of hard work, so he's making me do all these lame chores."

"It's not lame, it's amazing!" Eris said, looking down at the floor, which was painted with a map of all of Chima. "I've seen a lot of these places while flying around Chima. But **wouldn't it be awesome to actually visit a few**?"

Laval looked up at her and grinned. They were both thinking the same thing.

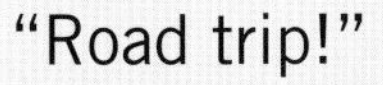

"Road trip!"

Minutes later, the two friends were speeding away from the Lion Compound in a Royal Fighter, a powerful vehicle with large treads designed for all-terrain travel.

"It's cool that your father let us drive his Fighter, Laval," Eris said.

Laval didn't answer, and she eyed him curiously. **"You do have permission, don't you?"** she asked.

"Uh, not exactly," Laval replied. "But he's out of town. What's the worst that can happen — *whoa*!"

Laval suddenly realized that the Fighter was perilously close to the edge of a steep cliff. He steered away just in time. Then he drove across the Grand Archway, a stone bridge, and nearly drove off the side. When he finally reached solid ground, a huge tree trunk dropped in front of the armored vehicle.

Laval swerved, just barely avoiding it.

"The Falling Jungle?" Laval cried. "I thought we were looking to hit some scenic spots . . . not have the scenic spots hit us!"

Laval swerved to dodge another tree, but they weren't out of trouble yet.

The next road took them through the swamps, where the Royal Fighter got covered in mud.

"Okay, I'm not the best driver, but it's still a pretty fun trip, right?" Laval asked.

"Yeah, as long as your dad doesn't see all that mud on his Fighter," Eris replied.

"Oh, don't worry. We've got lots of time to clean it up. Let's keep going!" Laval said, revving up the Fighter again.

He drove on until they reached the Shadow Hills, sloping hills shaped like the ancient animals that inhabited Chima before Mount Cavora changed them forever.

Laval rode up to the very top of the Lion-shaped hill. He and Eris got out to admire the view as the sun set over Chima.

"My father used to take me up here when I was young," Laval said. "'Best sunset in all of Chima,' he used to say."

"I won't argue with him there," Eris said. "And speaking of your father . . ."

"Don't worry," Laval said. "His Royal Fighter's fine."

"I know," Eris agreed. "With the parking brake on, that things not going anywhere."

"Uhh . . . what parking brake?" Laval asked.

They turned to see the Fighter slowly rolling down the hill. With a cry, Laval and Eris charged after it, but they were too late. The Fighter picked up speed as it slid down the steep slope, smashing into the rocks below.

"Oh, no!" Laval yelled. "My dad's gonna totally flip out. What do we do now?"

"Don't worry," Eris said. "I've got an idea."

Eris was good at solving problems, so Laval followed her.

Night fell on Chima as the two friends went to seek help. Soon they reached a village with a sign showing a picture of a Beaver at the entrance.

"Beavers? That's your idea?" Laval asked. But Eris kept going, leading him across a series of torch-lit canals and ponds.

"Supposedly, they can rebuild anything. And they love doing it," Eris promised.

As they drew close to the central Beaver Lodge, the canals suddenly opened up, flooding the area around them with water. Laval shivered; like most Lions, he hated water. As the water rose, menacing-looking Beavers swam out toward them.

"I hate water!" Laval complained. "What ever made you think they'd fix our Royal Fighter?"

The Beavers suddenly stopped swimming, and their leader, Breezor, stood up.

"Did you say you have a Royal Fighter that needs fixing?" he asked excitedly.

"Fix it! Fix it! Fix it!" the other Beavers began to chant.

Eris grinned at Laval. They had come to the right place!

It wasn't long before the industrious Beavers had dragged the broken Fighter into the lodge. They swarmed around it, happily working with their tools.

"Thank you *soooo* much for helping us," Laval said with relief. Once the vehicle was fixed, his dad would never have to know that it had crashed.

"No, thank *you* for driving so badly!" Breezor said cheerfully. He glanced back at the Fighter. "It's too bad the rest of the tribe isn't here. They would love this!"

"Where is everybody, anyway?" Eris asked.

Breezor motioned for them to follow him outside. They walked for a little while, and then he pointed up at Mount Cavora floating in the sky. The CHI flowed from the mountain onto the Cavora Font, a flat-topped hill underneath it, and from there, into the Lion Temple. Except now, a group of Beavers was building a dam, blocking the water from reaching the Sacred Pool!

Eris was horrified. "Did someone ask you to do this?"

"Yes," Breezor replied. "A Crocodile. The one up there on that cliff."

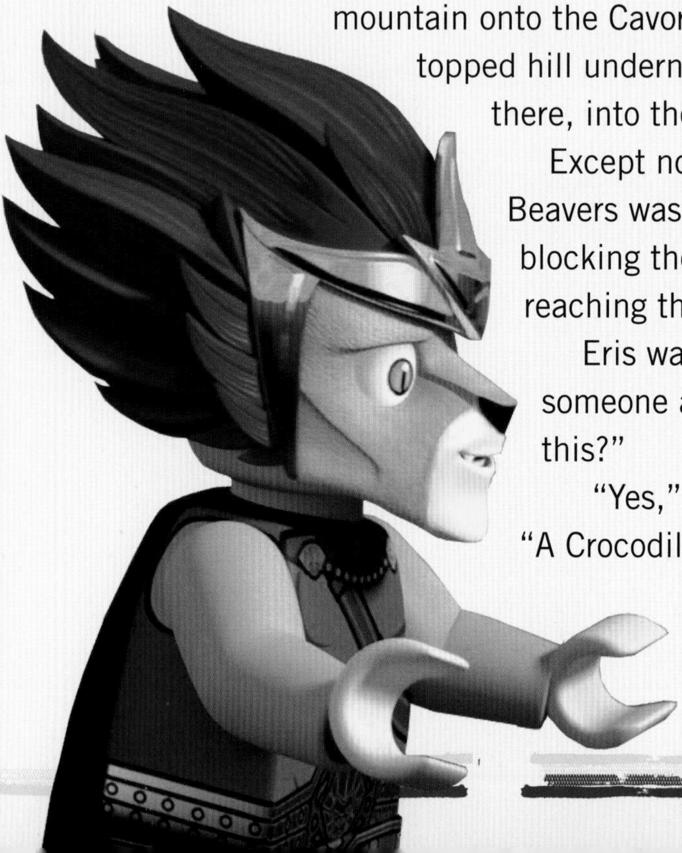

"Cragger!" Laval gasped. The Crocodile was overseeing the construction of the dam.

Eris frowned. "It gets worse. They're also building a canal to divert the CHI water . . ."

". . . to the Crocodile Swamp?" Laval finished in disbelief. "Are they seriously trying to steal our CHI for themselves?"

Suddenly, he felt a spear jabbing into his back.

"*Steal* is such an ugly word," said a menacing voice. Laval turned to see the Croc Warrior Crug behind him. Another Croc, Crawley, was jabbing a spear into Eris's back.

"We prefer to see it as more of a 'restructuring,'" Crawley said. "You Lions used to control the CHI, and now we will."

Then Crug took Laval's sword, and Crawley grabbed Eris's CHI Axe. Now the two friends couldn't fight back.

"Can this road trip get any worse?" Laval moaned.

Crug and Crawley marched Laval and Eris up to the Cavora Font, leaving Breezor behind. As they reached the waterfall, they heard a loud roar.

"That's the Lion's Distress Roar!" Eris said excitedly. "Laval, your dad must have seen the dam. He'll be here soon in his . . . Royal Fighter?"

Laval sighed. "Yup. Things just got worse."

Then he felt the spear in his back again. "Move along!" Crug said.

Laval shook his head as they walked up the hilly path to the base of the waterfall. "I really messed up this time," he muttered. "Even if Dad makes it here in time, he'll find out about his busted Fighter. *Ughhh!*"

A Beaver working nearby perked up. "Did you say you have a Royal Fighter that needs fixing?"

More Beavers rushed over.

"**Wow!** I've always wanted to work on one of those Royal Fighters!" said another worker.

Crug and Crawley pushed the Beavers aside. "Out of the way. We're taking these prisoners to see the boss."

"Awwwwww!" whined the disappointed Beavers.

That gave Eris an idea. "You probably wouldn't want to work on this Royal Fighter anyway. It needs to be *completely* rebuilt."

Laval caught on. "Yeah, and it's a real rush job."

The Beavers shuddered with excitement. "Completely rebuilt? A rush job? *Ohhhhh!*"

The rest of the Beavers working on the dam scampered over to see what the excitement was about.

"All that work! Oh, glorious work!" they chattered.

From his perch on a cliff above them, Cragger noticed the Beavers abandoning the dam.

"What is going on over there?" he asked angrily, his yellow eye flashing. He moved to the edge and looked down. "Laval? Eris? Guards, bring them to me NOW!"

Crawley tried to push the Beavers aside.

"Step aside, Beavers!" he ordered.

But the Beavers were too excited now. They swarmed around Laval, Eris, and the Crocs, wanting to hear more about the Royal Fighter. Laval nodded to Eris, and they acted quickly, spinning around and grabbing their weapons back from Crug and Crawley.

The foreman of the Beaver Dam rushed up to them.

"What's going on here?" he demanded.

"We're just trying to clear a path to the lodge where the broken Royal Fighter is," Eris said innocently.

That's all the Beavers needed to hear. All of them — even the foreman — jumped onto planks and rode the waters down the mountain like they were riding a giant water slide.

Cragger jumped down in front of Eris and Laval.

"Laval! Do you have to ruin everything I do?" Cragger asked angrily.

"No," Laval said. "Sometimes I let Eris ruin stuff, too."

He nodded at Eris, who threw her CHI Axe at the wood

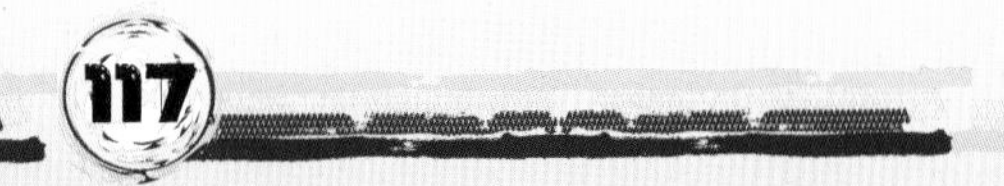

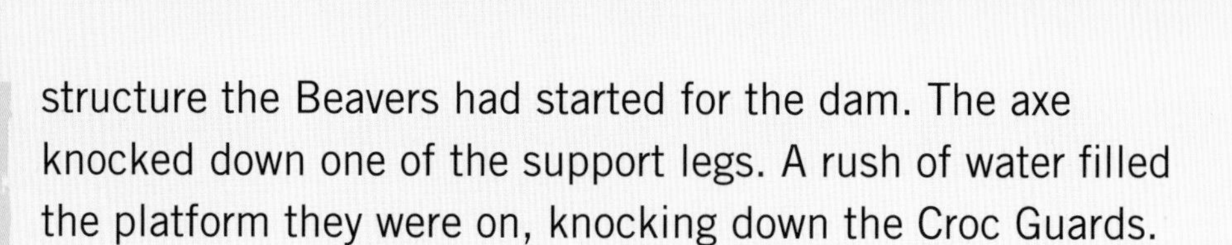

structure the Beavers had started for the dam. The axe knocked down one of the support legs. A rush of water filled the platform they were on, knocking down the Croc Guards.

Cragger jumped aside just in time. He lunged at Laval with his spear. "You're finished!" he growled.

Laval raised his sword, blocking him. The two former friends exchanged blows as they moved up the slippery slope to the cliff face overhead. Eris flew over to the dam, taking down more of the support beams with her axe.

"Did you really think you could steal all the CHI for yourself?" Laval asked, striking out with his sword.

"I'd share some with my allies," Cragger replied, blocking the blow with his spear.

"But that CHI belongs to everyone," Laval reminded him.

"Then everyone will need to ally with *me*!" cried Cragger as their weapons clanged. "Because once I re-route all this water to my swamp, we'll be the only CHI game in town."

"It's not a game! It's the life-force of all Chima!" Laval cried, and he and Cragger clashed weapons again.

Over at the dam, Eris was trying to take

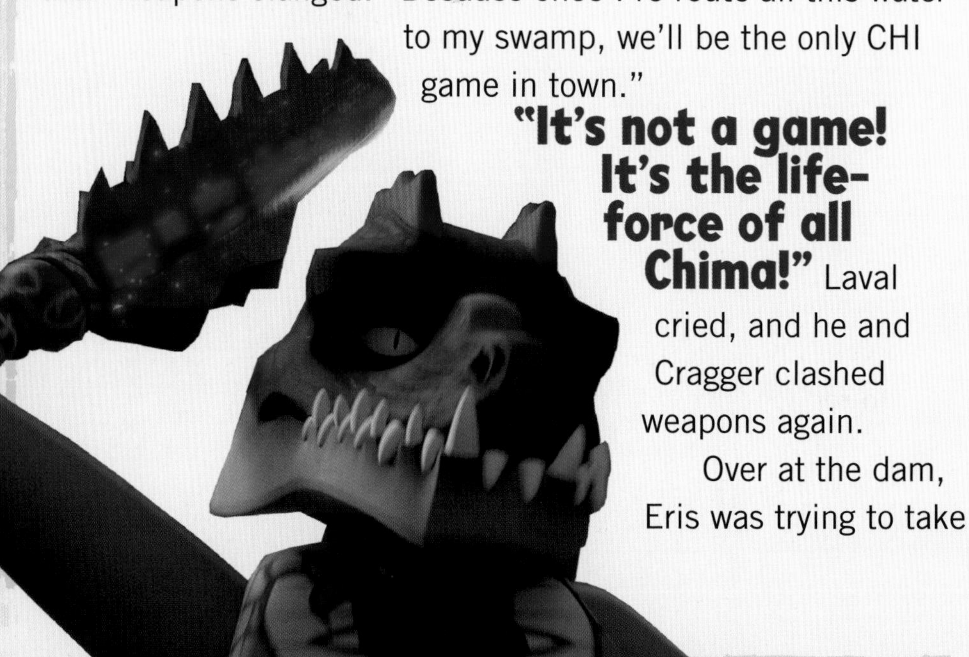

down the supports. As she reached for another log, the "log" turned around.

"Surprise!"

It wasn't a log — it was Crooler, Cragger's sister and Eris's old friend.

"Crooler? What are you doing?" Eris asked.

"Something my brother should have done long ago," Crooler growled. She lashed out at Eris with her Croc o' Nine Tails whip, and Eris countered with her CHI Axe.

Down below, Laval and Cragger were still locked in battle as the water rose around them. Laval struggled to stay on the last bits of dry land.

"It's interesting," Cragger said. "All this precious CHI you fight for comes from water, yet none of you Lions can swim."

"I don't have to swim to beat you," Laval shot back, but Cragger jumped into the water, swam behind Laval, and attacked him. Laval turned around just in time to deflect the blow, but he knew he was losing ground fast.

Up at the dam, Crooler lashed out at Eris again, but Eris flew up to avoid the blow. Then she swooped down and grabbed another piece of the dam.

"You think you're so smart, don't you?" Crooler asked angrily.

"I don't know," Eris said. "I'm just trying to redirect the three-point construction cantilevers of this elevated embankment to reduce diversionary hydro-flow."

Crooler looked confused. "Huh?"

"Translation: I'm busting your dam wide open!" Eris cried.

She dove down and pulled out another huge piece of the dam's supports.

A small, spurting hole opened in the bottom of the dam, nearly dousing Laval down below. Cragger took advantage and swam around Laval, leaping in and out of the water to attack the Lion again and again.

Exhausted, Laval sank to his knees. He had fought with all his might, but Cragger had the advantage. He glared up at his old friend as Cragger slowly approached him, his spear raised.

At the same time, Eris delivered a hard-hitting aerial kick to Crooler. She fell off the dam and plummeted down. . . .

"Eeeeeeek!"

Crooler landed right on top of her brother. *Wham!*

Laval mustered his strength and stood up, clutching his sword.

Before he could make a move, Crooler pulled a CHI Orb from under her cape.

"Cragger, take this CHI," she said, handing it to her brother. "I was saving it for something special."

Cragger grinned. With the burst of CHI power, nothing Laval could do would stop him. He moved to place it in the harness on his chest . . .

"Hey!"

Eris's CHI Axe came flying through the air, knocking the orb out of Cragger's hands! It rolled right to Laval's feet.

"Everyone out of here!" Eris yelled. "The whole dam's about to collapse."

Laval looked up to see water spouting out of dozens of holes in the dam. The whole structure was wobbling wildly.

"We'll have to settle this some other time, Cragger," Laval told his former friend.

But Cragger jumped over to Laval and reached to grab the CHI. "Never!" he cried.

"What are you doing?" Laval asked in disbelief. "Your dam's about to crush us all!"

"No," Cragger replied darkly. **"I'm about to crush you."**

He placed the CHI Orb in his chest harness, and his body began to glow with CHI power. A shining image of his inner CHI Warrior rose up behind him. The energy wave hit the dam up above, making it even unsteadier. . . .

"Aaaaaaaah!"

CHI-powered Cragger jumped up, waving his spear. But there was so much power running through him that he jumped too high, hitting the bottom of the dam.

***Bam!* The CHI power burst as Cragger hit the dam.** The small holes quickly spread, forming one giant hole that gushed water.

A massive wave of water poured from the dam, sweeping away Laval, Cragger, and Crooler with it.

Eris flew overhead. "Laval!" she screamed.

The water swept down the sides of the Cavora Font and rushed into the Sacred Pool in the Lion Temple. The Temple was soon overflowing with water and debris. The wave deposited Laval on the Temple floor, and then slowly receded.

Groggily, Laval opened his eyes to see the Temple filled with Lion Guards. Cragger, still powered with CHI, used his remaining strength to scramble over the Temple wall, carrying his sister with him.

Then Laval's eyes closed again. . . . He was *soooo* tired.

When Laval woke again, he was in his own bed. He sat up with a start. **"The CHI! My dad's Fighter!"** he yelled.

He started to leap out of bed when he felt Eris's wing on his shoulder. She gently pushed him back down.

"Relax," she said. "Everything's fine. The dam's gone, CHI's flowing, and your dad's Fighter is totally fixed, thanks to the Beavers. They even drove it back here and parked it for you."

"That was nice of them," Laval said. Those Beavers had gone to a lot of trouble for him. "And I still haven't even finished cleaning the map room. . . ."

Inspired by the Beavers, Laval headed right to the map room with Eris.

"I should have done this long ago," Laval said, happily

sweeping the floor, "instead of secretly taking my dad's Fighter on that road trip."

"Yeah, **but if we hadn't broken the rules, we never would've stopped Cragger's plot**," Eris pointed out.

Laval nodded. "You're right."

"Anyway, about that Fighter," Eris said. "You know how excited the Beavers were to fix it? Well . . . they might have made a few improvements."

Laval suddenly felt worried. "What kind of improvements?"

Down in the parking area, King LaGravis studied his Royal Fighter. It looked suspiciously shiny and perfect. But that wasn't all that was new. Two large teeth extended from the front of the Fighter, and a large, flat tail swung from the rear.

LaGravis had a feeling he knew who to blame.

"Lavaaaallll!"

EXPLORE CHIMA™ INTERACTIVELY

LEGENDS OF CHIMA™ ONLINE

Visit LEGO.com to explore Chima™ online . . . and battle for the CHI!

Build your own Chima world

Stake out your own part of Chima, and then collect and create buildings there! Each building you place gives you special powers and abilities.

Explore the Falling Jungle

Uncover the secrets of the forest, then battle the Crocs and their many allies. You'll find treasure and earn rewards . . . but look out for traps!

Build your arsenal online

Use LEGO® bricks to create your own virtual CHI Weapons!

Help Laval, Eris, and Gorzan

Laval and his friends need *you* to battle the Crocs. Meet your friends online and work together to defeat those who would steal CHI!

RACE THROUGH CHIMA IN SPEEDORZ™!

Customize your animal Minifigure, hop on a Speedor, and start racing! Unleash the CHI to boost your power and compete for the Tribe Cup. Play at LEGO.com or download the app.

PLAY LAVAL'S JOURNEY ON NINTENDO 3DS™

Discover the Legend of the Triple-CHI Armor!

Compete against Cragger to unlock the secret of the legendary triple-CHI armor. Explore the Lion Temple, Eagle Spire, Gorilla Forest, Rhino Quarry, Croc Swamp, and more! Harness the power of CHI to leap, swing, fly, and fight through fifteen levels of intense action.

Uncover the truth about the legend of the triple-CHI . . . before it's too late!